4 741268 000

The New Baby

Kate Petty, Lisa Kopper and Jim Pipe

Aladdin/Watts

London • Sydney

© Aladdin Books Ltd 2008

Designed and produced by
Aladdin Books Ltd
PO Box 53987
London SW15 2SF

First published in 2008
by Franklin Watts
338 Euston Road
London NW1 3BH

Franklin Watts Australia
Level 17/207 Kent Street
Sydney NSW 2000

A catalogue record for
this book is available
from the British Library.

Dewey Classification:
306.875

ISBN 978 0 7496 8626 0

Franklin Watts is a division of Hachette Children's Books,
an Hachette Livre UK company.
www.hachettelivre.co.uk

Illustrator: Lisa Kopper

Photocredits: All photos from istockphoto.com.

About this book

New experiences can be scary for young children. This series will help them to understand situations they may find themselves in, by explaining in a friendly way what can happen.

This book can be used as a starting point for discussing issues. The questions in some of the boxes ask children about their own experiences.

The stories will also help children to master basic reading skills and learn new vocabulary.

It can help if you read the first sentence to children, and then encourage them to read the rest of the page or story. At the end, try looking through the book again to find where the words in the glossary are used.

Contents

Sam's Mum has got a very big stomach.
Sam can't sit on her lap now.

"Never mind," says Mum,
"I won't be like this for much longer."

Sam leans against Mum instead and they make themselves comfortable.

He feels the baby kicking inside her. Perhaps the baby enjoys stories too!

You can feel a baby kicking inside its mother.

5

Mum gets things ready for the baby.
"Was I ever this little?" asks Sam.

"Yes," says Mum, "I'll find some photos
of you when you were tiny."

Sam laughs. "Wasn't I funny?"

"Little babies are often funny," says Mum.
"I expect this baby will make you
laugh sometimes."

Dad is taking Mum to the hospital because the baby is ready to be born.

Dad calls Sam's friends and they come to take him to the park.

8

Would you like a new brother or sister?

When Sam gets home, Granny is there to give him his supper.

Granny lets him skip his bath tonight and doesn't mind if he stays up late!

"Wake up, Sam!" Dad hasn't slept at all.

"You've got a baby sister!" says Dad.
"We think we'll call her Jenny.
How do you like that name?"

They stop for presents on the way
to the hospital. "Hurry up, Sam,
Mum's waiting." Sam chooses a panda
for the baby and some flowers for Mum.

At the hospital they go up in a lift.

Sam can hear the newborn babies as soon as the doors open.

Newborn babies can make a lot of noise!

12

"Where's the baby?" She's just waking up.

Sam gazes at his tiny new sister.
She's very small and rather wrinkled.
"Hello, Jenny," says Sam.

Today they bring Mum and Jenny home.
Sam is glad to have Mum back.
He's looking forward
to showing Jenny his things.

14

But Jenny goes straight to bed.
So does Mum! Dad is busy
so Sam helps himself to a drink. Oops!

Dad decides it's time for a cuddle.

You can help
at bathtime.

Jenny keeps Mum and Dad very busy.
She needs to be bathed...
and changed... and fed...
and changed again.

Sometimes they wish
she'd go to sleep.

16

Jenny has lots of visitors.
She has lots of presents too.
The rattle doesn't stop her crying.
But presents always cheer Sam up!

Jenny is dressed to go out today.
Sam and Dad are taking her for a walk.

Be careful with the pram!
It's hard work getting it down the steps.

18

The neighbours stop to
look at the baby.
Sam feels quite proud of her.

Sam pushes the pram.
Jenny falls asleep.
Well done, Sam.

It is fun to push a
pram or pushchair.

Sam talks to Jenny as Dad changes her nappy.
She watches him all the time.

Sam laughs at the funny faces she makes.
It's her bedtime at last.

"Come and sit on my lap, Sam," says Mum.

Mum reads Sam a bedtime story.
Sam can't imagine life without Jenny but
sometimes it's nice to have Mum all to himself.

cuddle

Mum
and
baby

crying

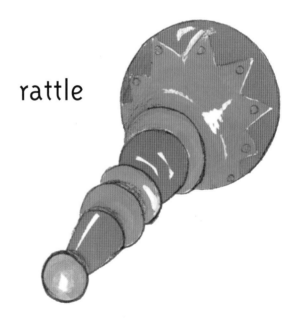

rattle

22

basket

baby lotion

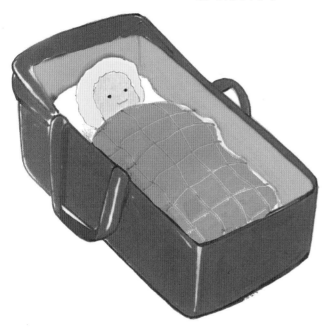

reading
a story

nappy

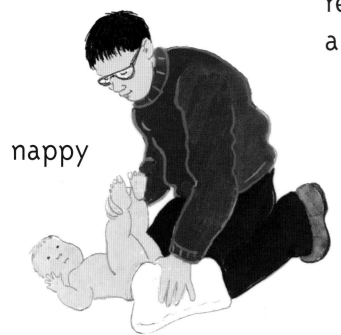

Index

Find out more

Find out more about a new baby in the family at:

www.kidshealth.org
www.raisingkids.co.uk
www.childcareaware.org
www.parenthood.com